Early Readers

Six Read Aloud Stories

Stories by Gill Davies

Illustrations by: Gill Guile, Stephen Holmes,
Jane Swift and Lawrie Taylor

Contents

Brown Watson

ENGLAND LE8 0HG

TIGER THINKS HARD

Tiger sits.

He sits and he thinks.

He sits and he thinks hard and he looks all around him.

Then he says:
"Oh, I am such an ordinary little tiger. I wish that I had pretty spots like you, Snake. I wish that I was tall like you, Giraffe. I wish that I could run as fast as you, Zebra."

Snake slides up the tree.

Tiger says, "Oh you are lucky, Snake. I wish I could go to the top of a tree and look at the sky from up there."

"But you are lucky too, Tiger," says Zebra:
"You can roar. You can run on your four fast legs and you have nice black stripes – just like me!"

Then two little frogs talk
to Tiger.

"You are so lucky," the frogs
say to him. "You are so big.
You are so much bigger than we
are."

"I am," says Tiger. Tiger thinks
hard and then he says, "Yes, I
am very lucky to be me."

"We are all very lucky to be
us," hisses wise
Snake. "And yet
none of us are
the same."

KEY WORDS

a	sits
am	talk
black	than
he	that
him	thinks
like	wish
same	you
says	your

WHAT CAN YOU SEE HERE?

flowers

giraffe

zebra

tiger

snake

CHEERING UP LOLLIPOP

Father Bear tells Teddy that Lollipop Bear has a sore head today and cannot come over to play.

"Perhaps she will feel better soon," says Teddy. "Please may I take her something to cheer her up?"

"Yes," says Mother Bear. "That is a very good idea. Let's see what we can find."

The bears set off with lots of nice things in a cart. They have bread and jam and cakes.

"Hello," say some rabbits. "Where are you going?"

"To see Lollipop," Teddy tells them. "She has a bad head. We want to cheer her up."

"We can give her a nice sweet lettuce," say the rabbits. "Here you are!"

13

Now all the bears are at the house. Lollipop is outside. She smiles.

"I could hear you all coming down the road," she says. "So I have come out to see you."

Teddy shows her all the good things in the cart.

"How wonderful," says Lollipop. "I was feeling much better already but now I feel even better still."

KEY WORDS

all	let's
bad	lots
cakes	Mother
could	nice
Father	please
feel	something
good	teddy
head	things

WHAT CAN YOU SEE HERE?

rabbits

squirrels

house

cat

cart

HOME SWEET HOME

Anna and Harry want to play in the old caravan.
"This will make a great den," says Harry.

But Mummy tells them they can't play there.
"No," she says. "That caravan is very old. It might fall over. It is not a safe place to play at all."

So Anna and Harry play with a ball instead.

That night the wind blows.
It blows so hard that the hen
house falls down.

In the morning the hens are
nowhere to be seen. Anna and
Harry look everywhere.
"Hello, hens," they call.
"Where are you? The wind
has stopped now. Please come
back."

Then Anna and
Harry hear Dad
calling to them.
"Come and see
what I have
found."

"Here are all the hens," says Dad. "Safe in the old caravan."

"But Mum says the caravan is not a safe place," cries Harry.

"Safe enough for hens," laughs Dad. "They are not big and heavy and they don't jump about like you two do."

So the hens stay snug in the caravan while Dad mends their old hen house.

KEY WORDS

be	jump
but	morning
call	night
down	not
everywhere	place
hello	play
hens	this
house	want

24

WHAT CAN YOU SEE HERE?

fence

wheel

caravan

hen house

hen

HOW MUCH ROOM DOES A MUSHROOM HAVE?

Lily Ladybird is running away from the rain. She pops under a small mushroom and waits for the rain to stop and the sun to come out again.

A snail slithers up by her. "Is there room for me?" he asks.

"I don't think so," says Lily. "It is only a very small mushroom but you can give it a try."

Before long a butterfly asks, "Have you room for me?"

"Oh dear," says Lily. "It is only a very small mushroom but let's see what we can do."

Soon all three sit under the mushroom.

Next a baby owl asks if he can join them, too. "Oh dear," says Lily. "This is such a small place but we can try."

Now four sit there.

All at once the rain stops and the sky is blue again.

"I don't know how we have all fit under here," says Lily as they run, slip, and fly outside.

"I do. Look! The mushroom is very big now," says Owl. "The rain has made it grow."

"Well, what a good place we picked," says Lily.

KEY WORDS

an	have
baby	long
blue	once
but	only
do	sit
fly	sky
stop	small
give	sun

WHAT CAN YOU SEE HERE?

ladybird

mushroom

snail

baby owl

butterfly

HARRY HORSE

"Harry is a very fine horse," says the vet one day.

"Yes," says Mr Green. "And he works very, very hard on the farm all day long."

"It is the big show next week," says the vet. "Why don't you take Harry along?"

"Oh, yes, please, can we? Do say yes," begs Betty. "That will be such fun."

Now Betty is very busy.
She brushes Harry until his
coat shines. She finds bells
and bows to make Harry look
smart.

Then she takes Harry to the
show. He walks round slowly.
He is not sure why he is doing
this and looks a little sad.

"You look great, Harry,"
shout the children.
"You look very smart."

Harry likes the children so he smiles. He lifts up his head and trots around the ring again. Everyone cheers as Betty leads him off.

"Can I take these bells and bows off now?" says Harry. "They make me feel a bit silly."

Harry wins first prize. "I am very surprised," he says. "Perhaps it is good to look silly, sometimes."

KEY WORDS

again	round
am	she
farm	slowly
head	that
horse	very
make	we
now	will
please	yes

WHAT CAN YOU SEE HERE?

Harry Horse

cup

first prize

Betty

ribbon

FELIX THE FIRE ENGINE

Felix the Fire Engine is on show at the school. All the children come to see him. They like to ring his bell.

"He is very brave and strong," says the teacher, Mr Long.
"Just like me," laughs Fireman Fred. At last it is time to go.

"Can I come, too?" asks Jack. He jumps inside.

43

Fred drives down the street.

Then they see smoke . . . lots of smoke. It is coming from Betty Baker's home.

"Quick," shouts Fred. "Hurry."

Felix rushes down the street. Then Fred jumps out and runs into the house. He brings Betty out of the front door while Felix sends water shooting into the fire until it stops.

"Thanks, both of you,"
says Betty.
"My chip pan got too hot.
You were just in time."

She gives them some cake
and a cup of tea.

"Just what we need,"
say Felix, Fred and Jack.
"What an exciting day!"

KEY WORDS

bring	need
cake	school
cup	street
got	tea
his	teacher
home	time
I	too
Mr	while

WHAT CAN YOU SEE HERE?

fireman

fire station

fire engine

First published 2016 by Brown Watson
The Old Mill, 76 Fleckney Road,
Kibworth Beauchamp, Leic LE8 0HG

ISBN: 978 0 7097 2264 9
© 2016 Brown Watson, England
Reprinted 2017
Printed in Malaysia